Specials!

Changing Britain
1485–1750

Clare Baker

Acknowledgements

Other people's ideas and worksheets have been adapted, changed and developed to produce these resources. I'm afraid that not much is new, but it is tried and tested! I can't say where all the ideas came from, but I do know that student teachers, people on courses and in school have all provided inspiration at one time or another. So, I thank all the friends and colleagues whose work has contributed, over the years, to the making of this book.

Several activities, including the research task on page 7 and the work on Queen Elizabeth, were inspired by lecturers on a Schools History Project Course in Leeds.

The classification tasks and the picture from memory tasks were developed in response to the DfES 'Leading in Learning' pack.

The spitting image of King Henry has been developed from a resource produced by a student teacher from Sheffield University.

'Mary, Mary, quite contrary' and 'Married life' are adaptations of the excellent SEN resources produced by John Murray in 'Changing Britain'.

Thank you to the Doncaster Literacy Co-ordinators and to Judith Gill, Secondary English Consultant, for the resource sheet 'Work it out!' (page 32).

© 2006 Folens Limited, on behalf of the author.

United Kingdom: Folens Publishers, Apex Business Centre, Boscombe Road, Dunstable, LU5 4RL.
Email: folens@folens.com

Ireland: Folens Publishers, Greenhills Road, Tallaght, Dublin 24.
Email: info@folens.ie

Poland: JUKA, ul. Renesansowa 38, Warsaw 01-905

Editor: Nina Randall   Layout artist: Book Matrix, India   Illustrations: Tony Randell
Cover design: Holbrook Design   Cover image: Corbis

First published 2006 by Folens Limited.

Every effort has been made to contact copyright holders of material used in this publication. If any copyright holder has been overlooked, we should be pleased to make any necessary arrangements.

British Library Cataloguing in Publication Data. A catalogue record for this publication is available from the British Library.

ISBN 1 84303 970 2/978 1 84303 9709

Contents

Introduction

Specials! History have been specifically written for teachers to use with students who may struggle with some of the skills and concepts needed for Key Stage 3 History. The titles are part of a wider series from Folens for use with lower ability students.

Each book in the series contains ten separate units covering the topics needed to complete the theme of the book. Most units have one or more photocopiable resource pages and several activity sheets. These allow the teacher to work in different ways. The tasks are differentiated throughout the book and offer all students the opportunity to expand their skills. By using photocopiable writing frames and emphasising literacy skills, students will be able to access historical information more easily.

The teacher's page at the start of each unit gives guidance on the material and is laid out as follows:

Objectives
These are the main skills or knowledge to be learned.

Prior knowledge
This refers to the minimum skills or knowledge required by students to complete the tasks. As a rule, students should have a reading comprehension age of 6 to 9 years and should be working at levels 1 to 3. Some activity sheets are more challenging than others and teachers will need to select accordingly.

QCA and NC links; Scottish attainment targets
All units link to the QCA Scheme of Work where relevant and to the NC for History at Key Stage 3. There are also links to the Scottish 5–14 guidelines.

Background
This provides additional information for the teacher, expanding on historical details or giving further information about the unit.

Starter activity
Since the units can be taught as a lesson, a warm-up activity focusing on an aspect of the unit is suggested.

Resource sheets and Activity sheets
The resource sheets, which are often visual but may also be written, do not include tasks and can be used as a stimulus for discussion. Related tasks are provided on the activity sheets.

Where necessary, keywords are included on the student pages. Other keywords are included on the teacher's page. These can be introduced to students at the teacher's discretion and depending on students' abilities.

Plenary
The teacher can use the suggestions here to recap on the main points covered or to reinforce a particular idea.

Assessment sheet
At the end of the book is an assessment sheet focusing on student progress. It can be used in different ways. A student can complete it as a self-assessment, while the teacher also completes one on each student's progress. They can then compare the two. This is useful in situations where the teacher or classroom assistant is working with one student. Alternatively, students can work in pairs to carry out peer assessments and then compare the outcomes with each other. Starting from a simple base that students can manage, the assessment sheet allows the student to discuss their own progress, to consider different points of view and to discuss how they might improve, thus enabling the teacher to see the work from the student's perspective.

Look out for other titles in the History series, which include:
- The Romans
- Medieval Britain 1066–1485
- Industrial Britain 1750–1900
- Britain in the 20th century

Teacher's notes

Overview

Objectives

- Find out about the key events from 1485–1750
- Learn how to divide the past into different periods
- Be able to organise information in chronological order
- Develop research and study skills

Prior knowledge

Students may be aware of some of the events and personalities linked to this period. The activity does not depend on them remembering any particular details but see if you can tease out any of their prior knowledge.

QCA links

Unit 5 'How successfully did Elizabeth I tackle the problems of her reign?'
Unit 7 'What can we learn from portraits?'
Unit 8 'The Civil Wars'

NC links

History skills 1, 2a and 4a

Scottish attainment targets

For all units
Environmental Studies – Society – Developing informed attitudes
Strand – Social and environmental responsibility
Level D

Environmental Studies – Society – People in the past
Strand – People, events and societies of significance in the past
Level D
Strand – Time and historical sequence
Level E
Environmental Studies – Society – Skills in social subjects
Strand – Preparing for tasks
Level D
Strand – Carrying out tasks
Level D
Strand – Reviewing and reporting on tasks
Level D

Background

Teachers can influence what students learn by helping them to make connections between what they already know and what they need to know. In this unit, students collaborate to construct an 'advance organiser' that will help to prevent them from being overwhelmed with new information by providing a summary prior to starting this topic. The summary could remain on display while the students work on Britain 1485–1750.

Starter activity

Ask students what they already know about the Tudors and Stuarts from their work at Key Stage 2. Record their ideas on the board. Explain that they will be studying some of these elements in more depth. At the beginning of each lesson, ask them questions to help them to develop their knowledge and understanding.

Resource sheets and activity sheet

Give students the resource sheet 'Who's who?' Working in pairs, they should cut the pictures out, shuffle them and stick them onto an A3 sheet in chronological order. These images provide a visual framework for the work the students do throughout this topic.

Hand out the activity sheet 'Finding out' and a selection of text and reference books with information relating to Britain 1485–1750. (Two or three books for each pair will be enough.) The students should search the books for information, choosing and recording the date and a brief description of four events. Students should then cut out their research slips and add them to their A3 sheet, which has become an 'advance organiser', demonstrating the route through the rest of the course.

Students will have worked collaboratively to produce their 'advance organisers': spend some time reviewing how they have worked together and how they have learned in this activity.

Provide the resource sheet 'Timeline', which will serve as a personal record of the work done in this lesson. Ask the students to look at it and see how it compares with their own research.

Plenary

Play keyword hangman on the board to encourage students to use new words from the timeline.

Who's who?

Look at these characters from Britain 1485–1750.

Henry VII	**Henry VIII**	**Edward VI**
Mary I	**Elizabeth I**	**James I**
Charles I	**Oliver Cromwell**	**Charles II**

History Changing Britain 1485–1750

Activity sheet – Overview

Finding out

☞   With a partner, research this amazing period of British history.
Find any event between 1485 and 1750. Write the DATE in the space provided and
explain what happened in the EVENT box. By the end of the lesson, you will know
lots more about the topics you are going to study.

Changing Britain

Date:

Event:

Changing Britain

Date:

Event:

Changing Britain

Date:

Event:

Changing Britain

Date:

Event:

Timeline

	Henry VIII	Edward VI	Mary I	Elizabeth I	James I	Charles I	Cromwell	Charles II
Dates	1509–1547	1547–1553	1553–1558	1558–1603	1603–1625	1625–1649	1653–1658	1660–1685
Quote	"I have 6 wives."	"I'm a Protestant. I hate the Pope and the Catholic Church. I'll make everyone Protestant."	"I want everyone to be Catholic again. I have had Protestants burned for their faith."	"I can't find a suitable husband: I am married to England instead."	"I have a large family to support and I have huge debts left from Elizabeth."	"I believe in the Divine Right of Kings. God put me here to rule as I wish."	"I didn't want to be King, but in the end I accepted the title of 'Lord Protector'."	"I am known as the 'Merry Monarch', but I have had a hard life really!"
	Henry quarrelled with the Pope because he wouldn't give Henry a divorce.	Edward had a group of Protestant advisers to help him rule.	Mary married Philip, King of Spain. He kept having affairs.	Elizabeth was a very successful ruler, but she was threatened by Mary, Queen of Scots.	James became King of Scotland in 1567 when he was just one year old.	The Civil War between Royalists and Parliament lasted from 1642 to 1646.	Cromwell ruled through Parliament, but needed help from the army.	Plague struck London in 1665. The Great Fire destroyed large parts of London in 1666.
	Henry made himself Head of the Church in England and then gave himself a divorce.	Edward changed the way churches looked and enforced services in English.	Mary wanted children, but kept having miscarriages.	Catholics in Europe attacked England, but the Spanish Armada was defeated.	The Gunpowder Plot was a Catholic plan to kill James and to blow up the Houses of Parliament.	Charles was executed for treason in 1649.	Some people said that the world turned upside down when Cromwell ruled England.	Samuel Pepys, who worked for the Navy, kept a diary about life at this time.

History Changing Britain 1485–1750

Teacher's notes

Meet the Tudors

Objectives

● Find out more about the Tudors
● Collect information from a variety of sources

Prior knowledge

Students will have studied the Tudors at primary school. These activities should help to remind them of their work, without being dependent on their knowledge.

QCA links

Unit 5 'How successfully did Elizabeth I tackle the problems of her reign?'
Unit 7 'What can we learn from portraits?'

NC links

History skills 4a, 5a, 5b and 5c

Scottish attainment targets

Environmental Studies – Society – People in the past
Strand – People, events and societies of significance in the past
Level D
Strand – Time and historical sequence
Level E
Environmental Studies – Society – Skills in social subjects
Strand – Carrying out tasks
Level D

Background

The five sovereigns of the Tudor dynasty are among the most well-known figures in royal history. Henry VII ended the Wars of the Roses between the Houses of Lancaster and York and founded the highly successful Tudor house. Henry VII, his son Henry VIII and his three grandchildren Edward VI, Mary I and Elizabeth I together ruled for 118 eventful years. The Tudor court played a prominent part in the cultural Renaissance taking place in Europe. This period also saw the turbulence of two changes of official religion, resulting in the martyrdom of many adherents of both Protestantism and Roman Catholicism. The fear of Roman Catholicism induced by the Reformation was to last for several centuries and to play an influential role in the history of the Succession.

Starter activities

Think, pair and share: students should work alone and write down three things they can remember about the Tudors. Encourage them to talk to a partner to see if they can add to their own list and then share their ideas with the rest of the class.

Show the students a page of classified adverts from a local or national newspaper. Have the adverts been sorted in any way? Can the students spot the patterns? Help them to understand that being able to organise things into different categories is a useful skill.

Resource sheets and activity sheets

Introduce 'Meet the Tudors' and go through the questions. The aim is for students to understand and retain the answers to these key questions. Learning homework could be set, in bite-sized chunks, with a mini-test in the next lesson. Send copies of the resource sheet home so parents can help to support students' learning. The same resource sheet could be used in a later lesson as a starter or plenary activity: cut the worksheet up into questions and answers and ask the students to match the pairs as quickly as possible.

The resource sheet 'Sort the Tudors out!' should be cut into sort cards. Working in pairs, the students should decide how to classify the information they have been given to answer the five questions on the activity sheet 'Put the Tudors in their place'.

The activity sheet 'Family portrait' allows the students to start to secure the knowledge they have acquired by using it in a new format. They should complete the speech bubbles.

The activity sheet 'Play bingo with the Tudors!' should be used to test the students' retention of information. They should fill in their copy of the bingo grid with any words or phrases from a list of about 12 provided by you. Then give definitions or questions so they can cross off the answers, until one student wins by getting three-in-a-row. Allow the students to use their resource sheets at first so they gain confidence and then play it again with less support.

Plenary

Write some of the key words from this unit on the board and play SPLAT! Two students stand by the board, looking at the words. Another student gives a definition or asks a question and the students should try to be the first to put their hand over the key word that provides the answer. Take turns until all the words have been used at least once.

Meet the Tudors

The Tudors ruled from 1485 to 1603. Learn the answers to these important questions carefully: they will help you as you work through this topic.

Question	Answer
1. When did Henry VII become King?	1485, having won the Battle of Bosworth
2. When did Henry VIII become King?	1508, aged 17
3. Name two things Henry was famous for.	• Having six wives • Making himself Head of the Church of England to make England Protestant
4. What were Henry's three children called (in age order)?	Mary, Elizabeth and Edward
5. What happened to Henry VIII's six wives?	They were: divorced, beheaded, died, divorced, beheaded, survived
6. What religion was Edward VI?	Protestant
7. Name two things Mary was famous for.	• She was a Catholic who had lots of Protestants killed, so she was called 'Bloody Mary' • She couldn't have children
8. What was Elizabeth I famous for? Give two examples.	• She didn't get married, but said she was married to England • Her sailors defeated the Spanish Armada
9. Why was Mary, Queen of Scots, executed?	She was plotting to get rid of Elizabeth and to become Queen of England herself
10. What religion was Elizabeth?	Protestant

☞ Ask a friend or member of your family to test you. How many did you get right? If you try the same test again later, you will find you have made progress.

Sort the Tudors out!

Henry VII 	Born: 1457 Became ruler of England: 1485 Married: Elizabeth of York Surviving children: Arthur, Margaret, Henry Religion: Catholic Died: 1509
Henry VIII 	Born: 1491 Became ruler of England: 1509 Married: Catherine, Anne, Jane, Anne, Catherine and Catherine Surviving children: Mary, Elizabeth, Edward Religion: Catholic, then Protestant Died: 1547
Edward VI 	Born: 1537 Became ruler of England: 1547 Married: never Children: none Religion: Protestant Died: 1553
Mary I 	Born: 1516 Became ruler of England: 1553 Married: King Philip of Spain Children: none but several miscarriages Religion: Catholic Died: 1558
Elizabeth I 	Born: 1533 Became ruler of England: 1558 Married: never Children: none Religion: Protestant Died: 1603

Put the Tudors in their place

Answer these questions using the sort cards from 'Sort the Tudors out!' Note that some characters will have the same answers.

1. What religion were each of the Tudors?

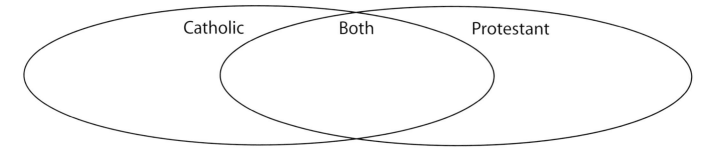

Catholic   Both   Protestant

2. Who ruled for the longest? Arrange them in order.

Longest reign   Shortest reign

3. Who had the most children?

Most children   Fewest children

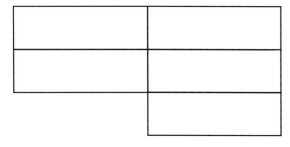

Edward VI   Mary I

4. Who married the most times?

5. Most marriages   Fewest marriages

6. Who lived the longest?

Longest life   Shortest life

Activity sheet – Meet the Tudors

Family portrait

Use your timeline and other resources to complete the speech bubbles for the Tudors. Write about when they ruled, what their problems were or who they were married to; colour your picture to make it look like a family portrait of the Tudors.

I'm Henry VII. I ruled from 1485 to 1509. My descendants ruled for 118 years.

Play bingo with the Tudors!

Look at the list of key words or phrases your teacher shows you. Choose nine and fill in your grid. Then it's eyes down to see who can get three-in-a-row first! Listen to your teacher's questions.

1.	2.	3.
4.	5.	6.
7.	8.	9.

Teacher's notes

Mighty monarchs: Henry VIII and Edward VI

Objectives

- Study Henry VIII and Edward VI
- Retrieve information from contemporary and modern sources

Prior knowledge

Students should be aware of the difference between primary and secondary sources. The information on the timeline will help them with the tasks about Edward.

QCA link

Unit 7 'What can we learn from portraits?'

NC links

History skills 2a, 2b, 3 and 5a

Scottish attainment targets

Environmental Studies – Society – People in the past
Strand – People, events and societies of significance in the past
Level D
Strand – The nature of historical evidence
Level D
Environmental Studies – Society – Skills in social subjects
Strand – Carrying out tasks
Level D

Background

In his youth, Henry was athletic, highly intelligent and a lavish patron of the arts. He wanted a son because he did not want to risk handing on the Crown to a woman, which might lead to domination by a foreign power through marriage. To get a divorce, he had to head the Protestant Reformation, which divided his family and the country.

Edward was brought up as a Protestant and introduced *The Book of Common Prayer*. He abolished Roman Catholic practices.

Starter activity

Model the process of crediting sources for the students by nominating a well-known public figure and asking students to describe the person to you, one detail at a time. Show each piece of information on the board as a picture. For everything you draw, make sure you add the name of the student who provided the detail. When the drawing is complete, 'mark' the finished product. Give yourself one mark for every feature you have drawn and three additional marks for every source you have credited.

Activity sheets

The activity sheet 'What was Henry like?' encourages students to search through sources for relevant information and to start to consider issues of utility and reliability of evidence. Close analysis of the activity sheet 'A spitting image of Henry' gives the students a chance to consolidate this understanding and produces good work for a display. They should use 'What was Henry like?' to complete the source labels in the picture. Confident students may prefer to make their own image of Henry based on the sources.

Before starting the 'Protestant propaganda?' activity, make these four points clear to the students:

- Henry wanted to remarry because his first wife couldn't have any more children and he wanted a son. He had to ask the Catholic Pope for permission to get divorced but the Pope said no.
- Henry was furious. He decided to make himself Head of the Church of England, to give himself a divorce and to remarry.
- Henry was pleased when his son, Edward, was born – at last he had an heir who could take over when he died.
- Edward was brought up as a Protestant. All his advisers were Protestants. They all hated the Pope. Protestants didn't like statues and paintings in church and they didn't like services in Latin. They said services should be in English.

This sheet helps students to scrutinise and interpret a complex contemporary source, while 'Reporting to Edward' allows students to demonstrate their understanding by completing the report based on 'Protestant propaganda?'

Plenary

Ask students to work in pairs to prepare a 30-second presentation on either Henry or Edward. Ask other students to give them feedback on their presentation, using the following sentence starters:
One thing I really like about your presentation is…
One thing you could improve for next time is…

Activity sheet – Mighty monarchs: Henry VIII and Edward VI

What was Henry like?

☞ Read these sources carefully. How much can you learn about Henry?

Source A

'He is extremely handsome and has now got a beard that looks like gold. He is very clever, a good musician, a fine horseman, speaks good French and is very religious.'

Venetian ambassador, 1520

This source contains ☐ pieces of information about Henry.

Source B

'He married six times in order to try to get a son and heir. He inherited his grandfather's love of fine clothes, food and drink and he inherited his grandfather's great size.'

Dr Starkey, 1991

This source contains ☐ pieces of information about Henry.

Source C

'He was a king who agreed to the murder of his own wives, servants and subjects, and who was responsible for smashing up more religious works of art than any other person.'

Rev Conlon, 1991

This source contains ☐ pieces of information about Henry.

Source D

'His selfishness, self-importance and tendency to sulk a lot sprung from a condition of a second-rate mind and a feeling that he was second best to other people. He ignored the good advice of his friends and wasted men, money and equipment on costly wars.'

Dr John Guy, 1988

This source contains ☐ pieces of information about Henry.

☞ Answer these questions on a separate piece of paper.

    1. Which source is most useful?

    2. Explain why you trust the information in some sources.

    3. Explain why you do not trust the information in some sources.

A spitting image of Henry

An artist has drawn a picture of King Henry using the information from the activity sheet, 'What was Henry like?' Sadly, this artist is not a good historian and has forgotten to say where the information came from! Help the artist become a better historian by writing source 'A', 'B', 'C' or 'D' in the spaces provided on the picture. An example has been done for you.

☞ You might like to draw your own version of this cartoon based on the evidence you have studied about Henry.

Protestant propaganda?

☞ Study this strange picture of King Henry, King Edward and the Pope.
Can you spot all the details listed below the picture?

Can you find these things? Tick the box if you can.   Tick here

Henry pointing at his son, Edward	
Edward sitting on the throne	
Edward's eight advisers in the room – seven sitting and one standing	
The Pope being crushed by a book	
A book that says 'The worde of the Lord endureth [lasts] for ever'	
The Pope being dragged away in chains	
Soldiers breaking a religious statue	
Four strange, empty rectangles	

☞ How would you describe Henry, Edward and the Pope?

History Changing Britain 1485–1750

Reporting to Edward

Imagine you are one of Edward's Protestant advisers. You have just seen the painting showing Edward with his father and the Pope. Complete this report telling Edward what you think about the painting's message. Choose the correct words where appropriate.

Dear King Edward,

I have just seen the **fantastic/dreadful** painting of you with your father and the Pope. Of course, this is an **imagined/real** scene, because there could never be two kings alive in the same room at the same time and the Pope never visited England in the 16th century!

Even so, I think the message of the picture is very **clear/confusing**.

King Henry is shown in bed, because the artist has imagined a moment near his death. You are shown sitting **happily/sadly** on the throne, while your father is pointing at you **anxiously/proudly**, as if to say, 'This is my son, who will be the next **Catholic/Protestant** King of Englwand'. The Pope is shown at the bottom of the picture, looking **confident/frightened** and **happy/cross**.

You are surrounded by serious looking men in dark clothes, some wearing gold chains. These are your loyal **Catholic/Protestant** advisers. They look like **weak/powerful**, **dishonest/honest** men.

The prayer book above the Pope's head is written in English. It says

_____

_____

I think this means _____

_____

_____

In the top right-hand side of the picture, I can see some **priests/soldiers** pulling down a statue. As a Protestant, I think this is a **good/bad** idea, so it is not surprising that the Pope looks sad and you look pleased.

This is an example of Protestant propaganda, making the new King look wise and powerful and the Pope look evil. It will help you to get your message across to the people of England. Keep up the good work!

Your loyal adviser

Teacher's notes

Mighty monarchs: Mary I and Elizabeth I

Objectives

- Study Mary and Elizabeth in more detail
- Study a range of historical evidence
- Understand the importance of propaganda in Tudor England

Prior knowledge

The timeline includes information the students may find useful before starting these tasks.

QCA links

Unit 5 'How successfully did Elizabeth I tackle the problems of her reign?'
Unit 7 'What can we learn from portraits?'

NC links

History skills 2a and 3a

Scottish attainment targets

Environmental Studies – Society – People in the past
Strand – People, events and societies of significance in the past
Level E
Strand – The nature of historical evidence
Level D

Background

Mary was a devout, courageous, stubborn and bitter Catholic, having been declared illegitimate when her parents were divorced. She tried to undo the Reformation, restoring Papal supremacy and reviving the old heresy laws. Three hundred Protestant heretics were burnt in three years. This made Mary very unpopular.

Elizabeth was well-educated, intelligent, determined and shrewd. Her 45-year reign is considered one of the most glorious in English history. She had astute political judgement and chose her ministers well. The popular image of Elizabeth's reign is one of triumph and success. The Queen herself was often called 'The Virgin Queen' and she cultivated this image very purposefully, presenting herself as a selfless woman who sacrificed personal happiness for the good of the nation.

Starter activities

Mary: Play key word bingo again (see activity sheet 'Play bingo with the Tudors', but don't let the students see their notes, timeline or the resource sheet 'Meet the Tudors.' They should be getting more confident about their ability to retain information).

Elizabeth: Show students a range of modern symbols that they can interpret quickly (for example, a McDonald's or Nike logo, school badge or religious symbol). Show them that they are experts in interpreting images. Explain that portraits of Elizabeth are hard for us to understand but that, at the time, people would have understood the symbolism in these images of the Queen as quickly as the students did the examples you showed them earlier.

Resource sheet and activity sheets

Most students will be familiar with the nursery rhyme, *Mary, Mary, quite contrary* but will not be aware of its possible origin as a cruel piece of doggerel. The resource sheet 'Queen Mary' gives the rhyme in full and provides an overview of Mary's life, while the activity sheet 'Mary, Mary, quite contrary' helps students to understand contemporary views.

'Portraits of Queen Elizabeth' includes information about why Elizabeth was concerned with her image. Students should search the portrait to find the symbols identified on the sheet. They could use colour pencils to shade the definition and the symbol in the portrait. Students could be asked to draw their own portraits of Elizabeth as powerful and fit to rule.

Plenary

Play 'Pictionary' with the Tudors. Students must think of a strong visual prompt for each of the four monarchs they have studied in detail. One student should draw their image on the board and the others have to guess who is being represented. Give them a time limit.

Use the assessment sheet (page 64) to help the students to identify their strengths and weaknesses as learners.

Queen Mary

Mary became Queen when her brother, Edward, died. She had lots of reasons for being unhappy, but Mary's unhappiness did not make her popular.

Lots of people hated her. They did not want to be Catholics. Some people were even prepared to die rather than give up their Protestant religion. Mary had so many Protestants burned to death that she was given a nasty nickname, 'Bloody Mary'. People mocked her by singing a cruel song about her.

We know the song now as this nursery rhyme:

Mary, Mary, quite contrary
How does your garden grow?
With silver bells
And cockle shells
And pretty maids all in a row.

'Mary, Mary, quite contrary'

👉 Write the words of the original nursery rhyme in the correct boxes. Look at the pictures and text to help you.

Mary had some baby daughters who died at birth and were buried in a garden.	Mary's husband kept having affairs. This was called 'cuckolding' in Mary's time.	Mary liked Catholic church bells at a time when these were unpopular with Protestants.	
Mary couldn't have any children – nothing could grow in her.			
Mary went against her father and brother and said England should be Catholic again.			

👉 Cut out and shuffle the cards. How quickly can you rearrange them?

History Changing Britain 1485–1750   © Folens (copiable page)

Portraits of Queen Elizabeth

Queen Elizabeth ruled for a long time – 45 years. This was tough for Elizabeth, especially as she got older. She needed to keep her people on her side. She wanted them to believe she was young, powerful, brave and loved serving her country. She had pictures painted of her that were full of 'secret' messages.

The 'Rainbow Portrait' was painted when she was 67. She doesn't look that old, but the artist was not a bad painter. He didn't want to show people what she really looked like, but that she was still a very good queen. He filled his picture with special messages. Look carefully to see if you can find them.

Based on the *Rainbow Portrait* by Isaac Oliver

The serpent shows that Elizabeth is WISE.

The eyes and ears show everyone SEES and LISTENS to Elizabeth and that she SEES and LISTENS to everyone.

The flowers are a sign of YOUTH.

The rainbow shows that Elizabeth brings PEACE.

The angel's wings show that Elizabeth is CLOSE TO GOD.

The long hair is a sign of YOUTH and VIRGINITY.

☞ Would Elizabeth be pleased with this portrait? On the back of this sheet, write one or two sentences as if you were the Queen saying thank you to the artist.

Teacher's notes

Who's who and what's what?

Objectives

- Find out more about some of the key historical characters of the 17th-century
- Learn how to collect information from a variety of sources

Prior knowledge

Students will have studied aspects of 17th-century life in primary school. Remind them of the Gunpowder Plot, the Plague and the Great Fire.

QCA link

Unit 8 'The Civil Wars'

NC links

History skills 4a, 5a, 5b and 5c

Scottish attainment targets

Environmental Studies – Society – People in the past
Strand – People, events and societies of significance in the past
Level D
Strand – Time and historical sequence
Level E
Environmental Studies – Society – Skills in social subjects
Strand – Carrying out tasks
Level D

Background

When Elizabeth I died, she was succeeded by James I (who was already James VI of Scotland), uniting the Crowns but not the governments of England and Scotland. Catholics plotted to blow up James and his Parliament in 1605.

Charles I could not work with Parliament and tried to rule without it. Eventually, there was a civil war in England that ended with the King's trial and execution for treason.

England was to be a republic until the collapse of Cromwell's Commonwealth and the restoration of Charles II in 1660.

In spring 1665, parishes began to report deaths attributable to the bubonic plague, which had already attacked London several times earlier in the century. By November 1665, when the epidemic ceased in

the cold weather, over 100 000 people had died. In September 1666, a fire broke out at night in a baker's shop in Pudding Lane, near the Billingsgate fish market in London. Fanned by a high wind, the fire quickly became uncontrollable and, in four days, the heritage of centuries was reduced to ashes. Two thirds of the city within the walls was destroyed, although the slums outside remained untouched.

Starter activity

Think, pair and share: students should work alone and write down three things they can remember about the Stuarts. They should talk to a partner to see if they can add to their own list and finally share their ideas with the rest of the class.

Resource sheets and activity sheets

Provide 'What do you know about the 17th-century?' and go through the questions. The aim is for students to understand and retain the answers to these key questions. Learning homework could be set, in bite-sized chunks, with a mini-test in the next lesson: cut the worksheet up into questions and answers and ask the students to match the pairs as quickly as possible.

The resource sheet '17th-century characters' needs to be cut into cards. Working in pairs, the students should decide how to classify the information they have been given to answer the five questions on the activity sheet 'Sort out the 17th century'.

The activity sheet 'Meet the heroes and villains of the 17th century' allows students to start to secure the knowledge they have acquired by using it in a new format.

The activity sheet 'Beat your teacher!' should be used to test the students' retention of information. Ask any nine questions from the 'What do you know about the 17th century?' resource sheet, challenging the students to get three-in-a-row correct. Make sure you ask three simple questions in an order that will allow all the students to succeed, boosting their confidence as learners.

Plenary

Use the sort cards from the resource sheet '17th-century characters' for a kinaesthetic activity: ask students to work in groups of five, with one set of sort cards per group. Announce the classification criterion, for example, age at death, and ask the students to pick a card each and to organise themselves in rank order. Ask the students to explain their decisions and award points to the group that completes the task first.

What do you know about the 17th century?

The Stuarts ruled England for most of the 17th century, although there was a very bitter civil war in the 1640s. Learn the answers to these important questions carefully: they will help you as you work through this topic.

	Questions	Answers
1.	Who became King in 1603?	James I. He was already James VI of Scotland.
2.	What was the 'Gunpowder Plot'?	A group of Catholics tried to blow up the Houses of Parliament.
3.	What happened to the captured plotters?	They were hanged, drawn and quartered – to punish them and frighten other Catholics.
4.	What does the 'Divine Right of Kings' mean?	James, and his son, Charles, believed God chose them to rule.
5.	When did Charles I become King?	When his father, James, died in 1625.
6.	Why did Charles hate Parliament?	Because every time it met, MPs grumbled and offered advice to the King – who did not want to listen.
7.	What is a civil war?	A war fought between people in the same country.
8.	Why did Parliament win the Civil War?	They had better leaders, an efficient army, the support of Scotland and money.
9.	When and why was Charles I executed?	Charles was found guilty of treason and was executed on 30 January 1649.
10.	Who ruled England after Charles?	The Lord Protector, Oliver Cromwell.
11.	What happened when Cromwell died in 1660?	Parliament invited Charles I's son, also called Charles, to be the next King of England.
12.	What happened in 1665?	A terrible plague killed thousands of people in London.
13.	What happened in London in 1666?	The Great Fire destroyed most of the city.

☞ Ask a friend or member of your family to test you. How many did you get right?
If you try the same test again later, you will find you have made progress.

17th-century characters

James I		Born: 1566

James I

Born: 1566
Ruled England from: 1603
Married: Anne
Surviving children: Three, including Charles I
Religion: Tolerant Protestant
Problems: Gunpowder Plot, money
Died: 1625

Charles I

Born: 1600
Ruled England from: 1625
Married: Henrietta Maria
Children: Nine, including Charles II
Religion: Protestant with a Catholic wife
Problems: Civil war and execution
Died: 1649

Oliver Cromwell

Born: 1599
Ruled England as Lord Protector from: 1653
Married: Elizabeth
Children: Five boys and four girls
Religion: Protestant
Problems: Should he be King?
Died: 1658

Charles II

Born: 1630
Ruled England from: 1660
Married: Catherine
Children: None
Religion: Catholic when he died
Problems: Plague and fire in London
Died: 1685

Samuel Pepys

Born: 1633
Ruled England from: Never
Married: Elizabeth
Children: None
Religion: Tolerant Protestant
Problems: Poor, argued with his wife
Died: 1703

Sort out the 17th century

Answer these questions using the sort cards from '17th-century characters'. Note that some characters will have the same answers.

1. What religion were these people?

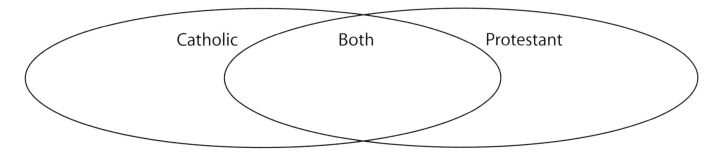

2. Who ruled for the longest? Arrange them in order.

Longest   Shortest

3. Who had the most children?

Most   Fewest

4. Whose problems were most serious?

Most serious   Least serious

5. Who lived the longest?

Longest   Shortest

Meet the heroes and villains of the 17th century

Use your timeline and other resources to complete the speech bubbles for the characters on this page. Write about when they ruled, what they did, what their problems were or who they were married to.

James I

Charles I

Cromwell

Pepys

Charles II

Beat your teacher!

1.	2.	3.
4.	5.	6.
7.	8.	9.

You will be asked nine questions. See if you can beat your teacher by getting three correct answers in a row.

I got ☐ answers right.

Teacher's notes

Danger! The Gunpowder Plot and Civil War

Objectives

- Read and understand some challenging text
- Test knowledge and understanding
- Work together to analyse a historical source
- Find out how some people felt about living without a king

Prior knowledge

The information from their timelines will help students tackle these activities.

QCA link

Unit 8 'The Civil Wars'

NC links

History skills 1, 2a and 2b

Scottish attainment targets

Environmental Studies – Society – People in the past
Strand – Time and historical sequence
Level E
Strand – Change and continuity, cause and effect
Level E

Background

The Gunpowder Plot

In 1605, a group of Catholic conspirators plotted to assassinate King James I by blowing up the House of Lords during the opening of Parliament. Enough powder was stored to destroy the building completely and kill everyone present. Guy Fawkes was tasked with igniting this huge bomb. His effigy still burns on 5 November bonfires.

The Civil War

The 17th century was a period of intense religious debate and radical politics. Both contributed to a bloody civil war in the mid-17th century between the Crown and Parliament, resulting in a Parliamentary victory for Oliver Cromwell and the dramatic execution of King Charles I. There was a short-lived republic from 1649 to 1653. A series of political experiments followed as the country's rulers tried to redefine and establish a workable constitution without a monarchy. Critics of the republic claimed that the world had been 'turned upside down'. Eventually, between 1653 and 1660, Oliver Cromwell acted as Lord Protector, refusing the offer of the throne.

Starter activity

Ask students to record at least three questions they would like answered by the end of the lesson about the Plot, using the five 'W' sentence starters: Who, What, Why, When and Where. Play key word hangman before working on the Civil War activities.

Resource sheets and activity sheets

The resource sheets, '1605' and 'Danger! The Civil War' contain some challenging words and ideas. Use 'Work it out!' to encourage students to identify any difficult words, work out how to say them and what the text means. The activity sheets, 'Danger! Conspiracy' and 'What do you know about the Civil War?' will help them, and you, to assess how successfully they have decoded the text.

The picture from memory group task, 'Can you remember?', encourages students to work collaboratively to devise and carry out a strategy to collect and reproduce information, helping to develop visual literacy. This can boost the self-esteem of students who are struggling with literacy and supports students with visual learning preferences while providing an opportunity for constructive group discussion.

Explain that each group has to decide on a collaborative system for getting the information from the picture of 'The world turned upside down' to the group diagram on 'Can you remember?'. Students have to take turns to visit the picture that has been 'hidden' from general view and then reproduce it as faithfully as possible on their group sheet.

You will need to think about where to show the picture – it must be out of sight of the groups when they are working together. You need to control the timing carefully – a timer that everyone can see is helpful. You may wish to enlarge the picture.

Plenary

Conduct a whole-class review of the different strategies used. Make a summary of these strategies at the end. Groups should be encouraged to explain their strategy during the plenary.

Resource sheet – Danger! The Gunpowder Plot and Civil War

1605

Treason, torture and terrible deaths! The Gunpowder Plot has it all.
Why were the plotters so bitter and what did they hope to achieve?

Background

Elizabeth was frightened when Mary, Queen of Scots, plotted to have her killed. She thought that all **Catholics were potential traitors**. They were forbidden to go to Catholic services and forced to attend Protestant churches, with steep fines for **recusants** who refused.

James had a Catholic wife, and Catholics hoped he would be kinder to them. He was to start with, but two plots were discovered in 1603 and James brought back the recusancy fines. Some Catholics were angry.

Robert Catesby led a group of 13 Catholics who conspired (or plotted) against James. The most famous conspirator was a man from Yorkshire, Guy Fawkes. The plotters planned to blow up Parliament and to kill the King.

Plan

The conspirators rented a cellar underneath the House of Lords and moved in 36 barrels of gunpowder, enough to blow everything sky high. Fawkes was to light the fuse, while other conspirators led uprisings elsewhere in England.

Events

Everything seemed ready. But on the night of 26 October 1605, an anonymous letter was delivered to one of the conspirator's relatives, Lord Monteagle, warning him to stay away from Parliament on 5 November. Guards found huge piles of firewood in a cellar and Guy Fawkes was discovered with the gunpowder. He was tortured and eventually most of the other conspirators were killed or captured.

Punishment

The surviving conspirators were tried in 1606. They were found guilty of treason and punished very severely.

- The traitors were dragged to the place of execution because they were unfit to walk on the earth.
- The traitors were hanged until they were half dead because they were unfit to breathe the air.
    - Still alive, their bowels and heart were removed.
    - Finally, they were beheaded and chopped into bits. Their body parts were put on show and eaten by the birds as they decomposed.

Resource sheet – Danger! The Gunpowder Plot and Civil War

Work it out!

☞ When you are reading, you sometimes have to deal with difficult words and challenging ideas. Try using these two strategies to help.

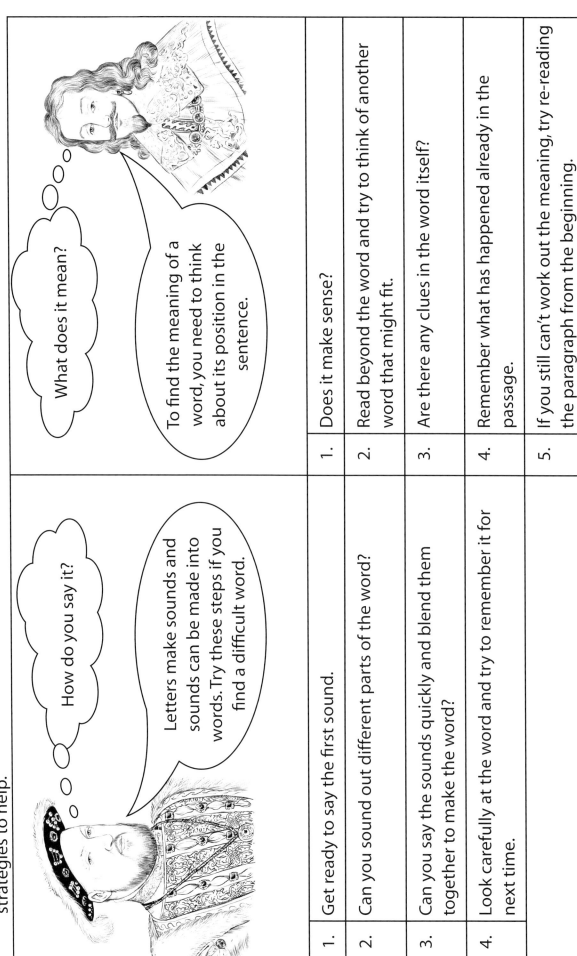

What does it mean?

To find the meaning of a word, you need to think about its position in the sentence.

1. Does it make sense?

2. Read beyond the word and try to think of another word that might fit.

3. Are there any clues in the word itself?

4. Remember what has happened already in the passage.

5. If you still can't work out the meaning, try re-reading the paragraph from the beginning.

How do you say it?

Letters make sounds and sounds can be made into words. Try these steps if you find a difficult word.

1. Get ready to say the first sound.

2. Can you sound out different parts of the word?

3. Can you say the sounds quickly and blend them together to make the word?

4. Look carefully at the word and try to remember it for next time.

Danger! Conspiracy

Remember, remember the fifth of November
Gunpowder, treason and plot!
I see no reason why gunpowder treason
Should ever be forgot!

Use this sheet to see how much you can remember about the Gunpowder Plot.
Tick the sentences that are true. Put a cross next to the sentences that are false.

1.	Guy Fawkes was born in London.	
2.	Catholics who refused to go to Protestant services were called recusants and could be fined.	
3.	The conspirators were all Catholics.	
4.	The plot was an attempt to kill King James.	
5.	Guy Fawkes led the plot.	
6.	There were 20 people involved in the plot.	
7.	The plot took place in 1503.	
8.	Lord Monteagle got a letter warning him not to go to Parliament.	
9.	Six barrels of gunpowder were found in a cellar under Parliament.	
10.	Guy Fawkes was exiled as punishment for his crime.	

☞ Check your answers using the resource sheet '1605'. For each of the sentences that you thought were false, write a new sentence that is true.

Danger! The Civil War

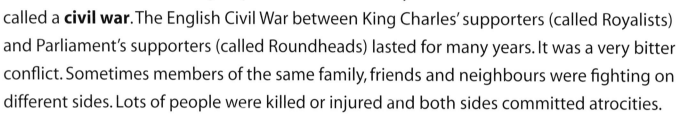

Charles I found it very hard to govern because:

- some people thought he wanted to make England a Catholic country again;

- he was always short of money;

- Parliament wanted more power.

By 1642, things had got so bad that Charles declared war on Parliament. A war between groups in the same country is called a **civil war**. The English Civil War between King Charles' supporters (called Royalists) and Parliament's supporters (called Roundheads) lasted for many years. It was a very bitter conflict. Sometimes members of the same family, friends and neighbours were fighting on different sides. Lots of people were killed or injured and both sides committed atrocities.

Eventually, King Charles lost the Civil War. MPs decided to put him on trial. They said Charles was 'a tyrant, traitor, murderer and enemy of the people of England'. Charles said God had made him King, so anything he did had God's blessing and no one should argue with him. Parliament disagreed; Charles was found guilty and sentenced to death.

On 30 January 1649, Charles walked to the place of execution. He wore two shirts because it was a cold day and he did not want anyone who saw him shivering to think he was shaking from fear. After making a speech claiming that he was innocent, Charles knelt and put his head on the block and was executed. People in the crowd groaned and some

fainted. Other people mopped up the King's blood. Later they said these blood-soaked cloths had the power to heal sick people.

Parliament's leader, a man called Oliver Cromwell, now made the laws and ran the country. Some people, who had supported the King, believed that the world had been 'turned upside down'.

☞ Use the strategies on 'Work it out!' to help you understand what this passage is telling you.

Activity sheet – Danger! The Gunpowder Plot and Civil War

What do you know about the Civil War?

Use the information from the resource sheet 'Danger! The Civil War' to write your own quiz about these amazing events. Remember to write the answers down as well, so anyone who tries your quiz can check their results.

Question	Answer
1.	
2.	
3.	
4.	
5.	
6.	
7.	
8.	
9.	
10.	

How well did you do?

☞ An artist has painted these pictures of the day of Charles' execution. Can you put them into chronological order? Write 1, 2, 3 or 4 in the boxes below the pictures.

The world turned upside down

The world turned upside down:

or a brief description of the ridiculous fashions of these distracted times.

History Changing Britain 1485–1750

Can you remember?

The world turned upside down:

Working in groups of four, try to complete this picture. You will only be allowed to see the picture one at a time, for just ten seconds each. You must work out a strategy for looking at the picture and for drawing as much detail as possible on your page. Good luck!

Teacher's notes

Enjoying yourself: Sport

Objectives

- Recognise that people in the past were very like us
- Interrogate visual sources
- Produce structured written work

Prior knowledge

Students do not need any prior knowledge to participate in these activities, although an awareness of modern sport and leisure will help them to make the connections between the past and present.

NC links

History skills 2a, 2b, 2d, 3 and 5a

Scottish attainment targets

Environmental Studies – Society – People in the past
Strand – Change and continuity, cause and effect
Levels C and D
Environmental Studies – Society – Skills in social subjects
Strand – Reviewing and reporting on tasks
Level C

Background

Children playing

Pieter Brueghel the Elder (c.1525–1569), who painted *Children's Games* in 1560, was one of the greatest artists of his time. His pictures of peasant life helped to establish genre painting and he also popularised works illustrating proverbs.

Cotswold Olympics

The Cotswold Olympics took place annually from 1612 for almost 250 years. The Olympics presented a magnificent spectacle. Competitors were summoned to the hillside by the sound of a hunting horn and took part in a wide range of sports, including wrestling, shin kicking, swordplay, horseracing, coursing, field events such as jumping, and throwing the sledgehammer and

bar. Music and dancing also had their place, while chess was played in tents. A distinctive feature of the hillside was a mock castle with fireworks.

Starter activity

Introduce the idea of entertainment by playing four rounds of hangman, covering different types of activity, for example, sports, hobbies and games.

Resource sheets and activity sheets

The activity sheet 'Enjoying yourself in the 21st century' helps students to make links with people in the past by recognising that having fun has always been important. Give out the worksheet and allow students to work alone for two minutes, writing down examples of entertainments we enjoy now. Ask them to record how many different ideas they have and then get them to work in pairs for two minutes to share their ideas. Record how many ideas they now have. Finally, the students should share their ideas in groups of four and report back to the whole class. Help the class to reflect on the process of thinking, pairing and sharing as a strategy for collaborative learning.

The resource sheet, 'Children playing', helps students to develop an empathetic understanding of another era by getting them to analyse a rich visual source. Enlarge it to A3 before giving to the students.

The activity sheet 'Children's games' gives students an opportunity to write at length about a topic they should feel confident about.

The resource sheets 'Picture from memory' and 'The Cotswold Olympics' and the activity sheet 'Cotswold Olympics frame' build on the experience students gained from 'The world turned upside down', although for this task the students are supported with a list of activities to look for in the picture.

Ask the students to peer mark the finished pictures, awarding one mark for each activity from the list and one mark for positioning it correctly on the picture.

Plenary

Students should work in pairs to prepare a mime or pose for one of the activities in the illustration of the Brueghel picture, *Children's Games*. The other students must try to work out which activity is being demonstrated.

Use the assessment sheet (page 64) to help the students to identify their strengths and weaknesses as learners.

Enjoying yourself in the 21st century

Make a list of entertainments for people living now. Can you think of one for each letter? An example has been done for you.

How many examples of entertainment did you find?
Working alone ☐
Working with a partner ☐
Working in a group ☐

A	
B	
C	
D	
E	
F	Football
G	
H	
I	
J	
K	
L	
M	
N	
O	
P	
Q	
R	
S	
T	
U	
V	
W	
X	
Y	
Z	

Activity sheet – Enjoying yourself: Sport

Children playing

☞ Look carefully at this amazing picture. It shows many different games being played by children in the 16th century.

When you find any of the examples from the table below, write the number on the picture.

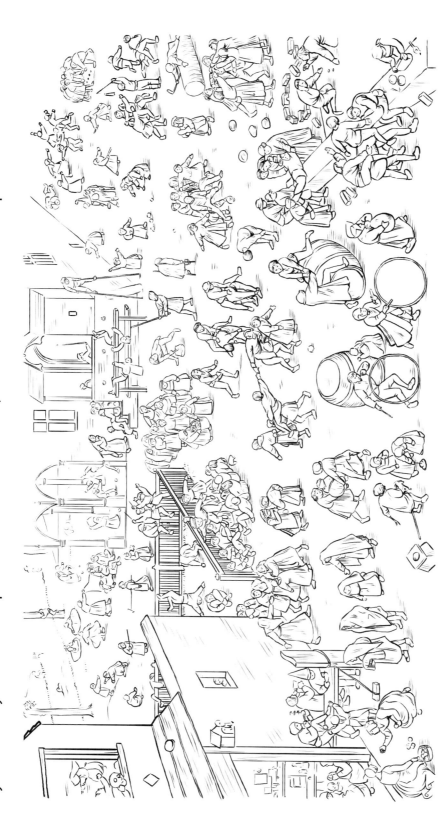

1.	A game using equipment	4.	A rough game	7.	A game we still play today
2.	A game for two children	5.	A calm game	8.	A game you've never seen before
3.	A game for a group of children	6.	A game that could be played indoors	9.	A game you'd like to play

History Changing Britain 1485–1750

Children's games

Answer this question using the work from the last two worksheets:

<u>Children in the 16th century didn't have as much fun as children living now. Do you agree</u>
<u>with this statement? Explain your answer.</u>

Give some examples

I disagree with this statement in some ways. Children living in the
16th century could enjoy themselves by_____

_____

_____

_____

_____

_____

_____

Give some examples

However, children living now have other ways of enjoying
themselves and can still do all the things children in the 16th
century did. They can_____

_____

_____

_____

_____

_____

Give reasons for your final judgement

Overall, I agree/disagree with the statement because_____

_____

_____

_____

_____

_____

Picture from memory

Your teacher will let one member of your group see a picture of 'The Cotswold Olympics' for just ten seconds.

This person must then record what they can remember on your group's version of the picture. Then another member of the group takes a turn to look at the picture.

Try to work out a strategy for this task. For example, you could send one member of the group to look at the top-left of the picture to see what they can find out, and then the next person could look at the top-right of the picture.

This is a list of what you are looking for:

Sword fighting	Picnicking
Cudgels	Dancing to bagpipes
Tossing the hammer	Leaping
Fox hunting	Tossing the bar
A mock castle with fireworks	Shin kicking with iron-tipped boots
Handstand	Horse riding

When you have finished, mark your work.
How well did your group do?
Think about which strategies worked best.
What will you do better next time?

☞ Now design a poster for the Olympics, including all the events you found on the original drawing. You could draw stick people. Remember to label all your pictures, so people looking at the poster know what to expect.

You might like to include people you know in the poster: for example, your teacher might be a champion picnicker, or perhaps a world-class shin-kicker!

The Cotswold Olympics

Cotswold Olympics frame

Working in groups of four, try to complete this picture. You will only be allowed to see the original picture one at a time, for ten seconds each. You must work out a strategy for looking at the picture and for drawing as much detail as possible on your page. Good luck!

History Changing Britain 1485–1750

Teacher's notes

Enjoying yourself: Leisure

Objectives

- Find out about 16th- and 17th-century beauty treatments
- Learn about the roles of London Coffee Houses
- Make connections between the present and the past

Prior knowledge

Students do not need any specific historical knowledge to participate fully in these activities.

NC links

History skills 2a and 2b

Scottish attainment targets

Environmental Studies – Society – People in the past
Strand – People, events and societies of significance in the past
Level D
Strand – Change and continuity, cause and effect
Level C

Background

Games were popular in Tudor times. Many of the games we play today are based on Tudor games, for example, hopscotch, draughts and playing cards. Children played Merelles in the 16th century.

Beauty Nits, lice and body odours are not glamorous and were not visible in the portraits of the time. Patches – artificial beauty spots – were worn by both sexes. Little bits of mouse skin could replace unfashionable eyebrows. Cosmetics were alarming. Ceruse, containing lead, produced a desirable matt white complexion, even on a smallpox-pitted skin, but it smelt, cracked and poisoned the wearer.

London Coffee Houses Francis Bacon warned the public of the dangerous properties of coffee in 1605. The first reference to a London Coffee House is from 1652, when Pasqua Rosee opened one, quickly followed by thousands more. They were important social venues where artists, writers, businessmen and bankers met. They were meeting places for religious or political dissidents and, in the mid- to late-17th century,
were 'under suspicion as being centres of intrigue and treasonable-talk'. Newspapers, journals and pamphlets were circulated so people could keep up-to-date on current affairs whilst drinking their coffee.

Starter activities

Games: Hand out the picture cards from a set of playing cards: the pictures are of kings, queens and courtiers like those at the Tudor court. Building on their previous work on 'Enjoying yourself', ask the students to write down other examples of games played by the Tudors and also by people in the 21st century.

Beauty: Make a list of all the beauty preparations that can be found in a modern home and use this as a starting point for a discussion about 16th- and 17th-century ideas about beauty.

Coffee Houses: Ask the students to make a list of all the reasons why people might go to a particular (local, if possible) coffee bar. Use this as a starting point for discussion about the various roles of London Coffee Houses.

Resource sheets and activity sheets

The resource sheet 'Beautiful ladies' provides information about 16th- and 17th-century beauty treatments, which can be discussed before the students complete the 'Make-up multiple choice' activity sheet. Cut out the 'Problems, problems' speech bubbles, giving one or two to each student. The writing frame 'Problem page' gives students an opportunity to write empathetically and at length about 16th- and 17th-century ideas of beauty. You may need to stress the importance of providing Tudor or Stuart resolutions.

The activity sheets 'The London Coffee Houses' and 'Inside a Coffee House' give students the opportunity to use written and visual sources to find out about the 17th century.

Finally, 'Come to my Coffee House!' allows students to demonstrate all their knowledge and understanding of this topic.

Plenary

Working in pairs, one student should argue that the 16th and 17th centuries were better for games (or beauty treatments or Coffee Houses), while the other should argue that the 21st century is better. Review their discussions with the whole class. Take a class vote to find the majority preference.

Beautiful ladies

Read this information about what women did to make themselves beautiful in the 16th and 17th centuries.

Women wanted to have:

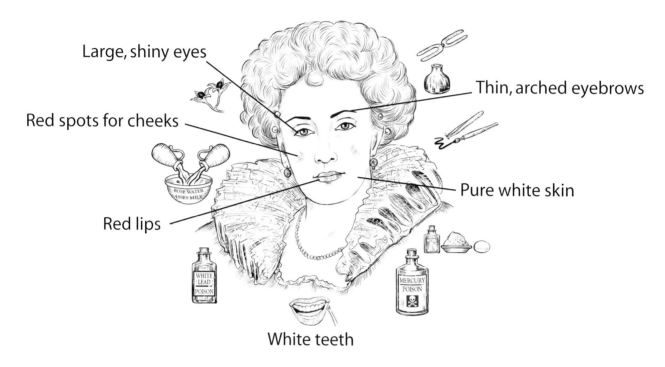

Large, shiny eyes

Thin, arched eyebrows

Red spots for cheeks

Pure white skin

Red lips

White teeth

To make themselves beautiful, women used the following beauty treatments:

1. Washing Queen Elizabeth was thought to be very clean – she had a bath every few months, even if she didn't need one! People hardly ever washed their hair, so everyone had lice and vermin.

2. Teeth People used a stick dipped in honey and salt to 'clean' their teeth. This removed the stains, but the teeth decayed and rotted away. Most people over 20 had horrible, smelly stumps instead of healthy teeth.

3. Face People used poisonous white lead as face powder, which made the skin crack, leaving open sores that would not heal.

4. Lips and cheeks First women 'roughed up' their skin to help the thick make-up stick. Then they used cochineal (made from crushed beetles and perfectly harmless) to make bright red lips and cheeks.

5. Eyebrows Plucked to very thin arches.

6. Hair Tightly curled and piled up on top of the head with jewels.

7. Bright eyes Women used a very poisonous drug to make their eyes shine and the pupils large.

8. Body odour Women used strong scents to cover the smell of their unwashed bodies, hair and rotting teeth.

9. Freckles and suntan These had to be hidden at all costs. Sublimate of mercury could be applied to the face. The skin would then peel off in strips, leaving unblemished skin.

Make-up multiple choice

Do you have what it takes to be a Tudor make-up adviser?

1. Was Queen Elizabeth clean?

a) No, she only bathed every few months ☐

b) Yes, bathing every few months is enough for anyone ☐

c) Yes, by the standards of her day, she was very clean ☐

2. What was the ideal colour for a woman's face, neck and chest?

a) Pure white with red cheeks ☐

b) A healthy tan and freckles were attractive ☐

c) A rosy complexion was best ☐

3. How did wealthy Tudor women clean their faces?

a) With soap and water ☐

b) With asses' milk and rosewater ☐

c) With white lead ☐

4. How did Tudor women clean their teeth?

a) With toothpaste ☐

b) With honey and salt ☐

c) With egg white ☐

5. Why did Tudor women use poisonous white lead every day?

a) To clean the bathroom ☐

b) To paint pictures ☐

c) To make their skin white ☐

6. What was used to make lips and cheeks shiny and red?

a) Lip-gloss and blusher ☐

b) Red powder made from crushed bark ☐

c) Cochineal – crushed red insects ☐

7. What would you expect to find in a Tudor's hair?

a) Curls, jewels and lice ☐

b) Ribbons ☐

c) Lice and mice ☐

8. What did Tudor women use for deodorants?

a) Antiperspirant sprays ☐

b) Strong scents ☐

c) Bunches of flowers ☐

9. How did sublimate of mercury help a Tudor woman keep herself beautiful?

a) She could peel off a layer of freckled or tanned skin ☐

b) She could throw it at so-called beauticians ☐

c) She could drink it ☐

Problems, problems

I've got dull eyes

My friends say I'm smelly

I've got bushy eyebrows

I've got freckles

I want my face to be white like Queen Elizabeth's

My cheeks aren't rosy and my lips are pale

My hair is lifeless and flat

Activity sheet – Enjoying yourself: Leisure

Problem page

☞ Imagine you are writing to an Agony Aunt in the 16th or 17th century about a beauty problem.

Dear Agony Aunt Anne,

Please help! My friends are teasing me because_____

_____

_____

_____

_____

_____

_____

_____

_____

I really want to impress Lord B at the Midsummer Ball next month. Please, please send me some advice – I'm desperate!

☞ Now see if you can write an answer using 16th- and 17th-century solutions.

Dear Desperate,

Stop worrying! There is a lot you can do in a month! I recommend

_____

_____

_____

_____

_____

_____

_____

_____

Enjoy the ball! Agony Aunt Anne

The London Coffee Houses

How many coffee shops are there in your local shopping centre?

Coffee shops are fashionable places to go nowadays.

The first Coffee House was opened in London in 1652. Soon there were dozens of Coffee Houses: everyone who was anyone wanted to be seen there in them. Why were they such important places?

 Read this source. Use four coloured pens to highlight the four main reasons people had for going to Coffee Houses.

> **There were lots of reasons for going to the new Coffee Houses in London. Firstly, London was an important business centre for the whole of England. Customers met at the Coffee Houses to impress the people they were doing business with. They could make deals there while drinking coffee. In addition, the Coffee Houses were good places to find out what was happening in the world. The first newspapers were being produced and they would be read and discussed over a cup of coffee. Another reason for the growing importance of Coffee Houses was that they gave interested people a place where they could meet to talk about politics. Some Coffee Houses even became the headquarters for the supporters of particular political parties. Finally, people wanted to be seen using the latest fashionable products. Drinking coffee and smoking tobacco using long clay pipes was thought to be fashionable.**

 Complete the key to help to make your notes effective. Colour the boxes using the same coloured pens you used to highlight the four main reasons above.

Key			
Doing business	Discussing politics	Catching up on the latest news	Being fashionable

Activity sheet – Enjoying yourself: Leisure

Inside a Coffee House

☞ Look carefully at the inside of a Coffee House. Can you see the following things?

- women handling cups
- a waiter pouring coffee
- a waiter collecting clay pipes from a box
- men using a candle to look at a painting
- men talking and looking at newspapers
- a huge pot of coffee boiling on an open fire

History Changing Britain 1485–1750

Come to my Coffee House!

Imagine you are opening a Coffee House in London in 1670. Design a poster to advertise your new Coffee House, encouraging fashionable people to come and spend their money.

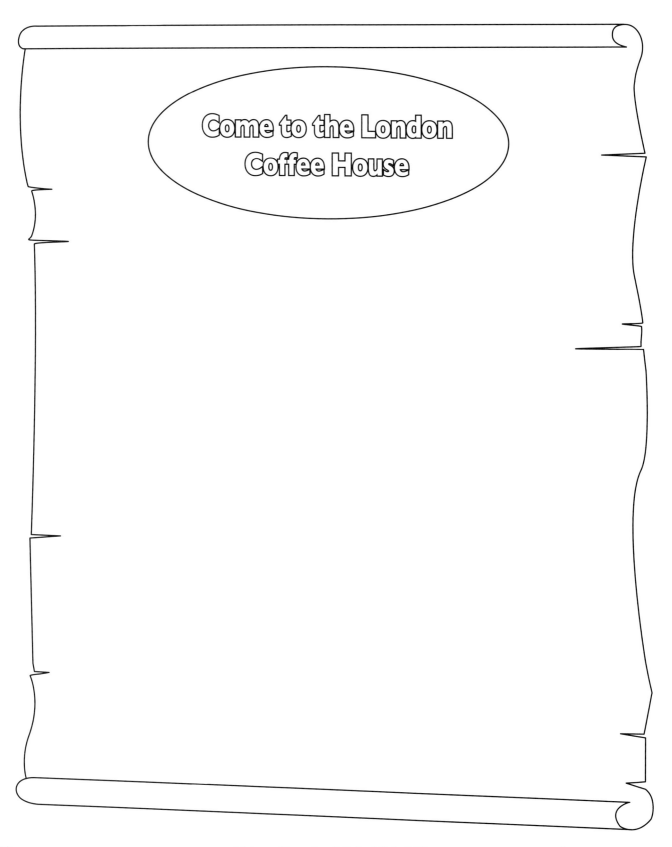

Come to the London
Coffee House

Teacher's notes

Mr and Mrs Pepys

Objectives

- Find out about the social life of an 'ordinary' couple
- Make inferences from a source in order to consider another person's feelings
- Develop reading skills by decoding 'difficult' text

Prior knowledge

Remind students that they have already found out about Pepys from the 'Who's who and what's what?' unit and from their timeline. They do not need any other prior knowledge to participate in these activities.

NC links

History skills 1, 2a, 2b and 5c

Scottish attainment targets

Environmental Studies – Society – People in the past
Strand – People, events and societies of significance in the past
Level D
Strand – Nature of historical evidence
Level D

Background

Samuel Pepys (1633–1703) is famous for his detailed diaries as well as for his public career as a naval administrator, secretary of the Admiralty, MP and President of the Royal Society. His diary covers both private remarks and detailed observations of contemporary events like the Plague of 1665 and the Great Fire of 1666. His marriage to the 15-year-old Huguenot, Elizabeth Marchant de Saint-Michel, came after a love match and together they survived early hardship, infidelities and jealousy.

Starter activities

To introduce the 'Gadding about' activity, ask the students to record everything they have done in the last week, including trips to the cinema, theatre, shops, church, outings to restaurants and playing games with friends. Use this as a starting point for analyzing Pepys' experience in January 1663.

To introduce the 'Married life' activity, ask the students to think about any soap opera they watch regularly on television. Tell them to think about one of the families. What do they quarrel about? Working in pairs, students should write a list and then share it with the whole class.

Resource sheet and activity sheets

Encourage the students to develop literacy and thinking skills by using a highlighter pen to identify key features of the activity sheet 'Gadding about'. The highlighted text then gives a colour-coded summary of a complex piece of text and should help students to develop confidence as readers.

The activity sheet 'Pepys' postcard to a pal' enables students to use the information they have just processed and to demonstrate their understanding in a simple and accessible format.

The activity sheets 'Married life' and 'Elizabeth's letter' allow students to work with original sources in a way that should make them feel more confident about their ability to understand and use challenging text, as a close study of the text is followed by reinterpretation of the information to help them to consolidate their understanding. These activities offer a rare opportunity to empathise with a woman from the 17th century.

Plenary

Play bingo (page 14) or 'Beat your teacher!' (page 29) again to help remind students of the forthcoming assessment.

Use the assessment sheet (page 64) to help the students to identify their strengths and weaknesses as learners.

Resource sheet – Mr and Mrs Pepys

Gadding about

At the end of 1662, Samuel Pepys made a new year's resolution to cut back on 'gadding' and to concentrate on his career. Look at his diary entries for the first two weeks in January. How successful was he in avoiding the temptations of the good life? Highlight these activities: theatre ● drinking ● cards ● eating ● relaxing ● shopping ● chatting.

1 January 1663
I went to see a tragic play, 'The Villain', for the second time. I enjoyed it, except the theatre was full of common people! I must stop gadding about and start work again tomorrow.

4 January
I went to church, but I wasn't impressed by the sermon.

5 January
I drank lots of wine from my wine cellar and then went out to eat with my Lord. We had a merry time. We played cards and then went to the theatre, but it was a poor play. Another game of cards when we got home, followed by supper, apples and beer before going to bed, with great pleasure, blessed be God.

6 January
I went to a book shop and looked over several good books and talked about them. Next, I went for a walk with an old friend and later I went shopping for a fine table for my dining room, costing me 50 shillings.
In the evening, I went to the theatre again to see 'Twelfth Night', which was acted well, but a silly play. Now Christmas is finally over and I have had a very good time. I have forgotten my promise to stick to my work, but from tomorrow I will work hard to get the money I need to sweeten my life.

8 January
I was longing to see a new play and so we went. The play was the best I have ever seen or think I ever will see. It had a very interesting plot.

11 January
I stayed in bed for a long time, chatting to my wife. Then we went to church. The sermon was dreadful.

13 January
Our friends came to eat with us. We ate an expensive feast (costing almost five pounds!) of oysters, rabbit and lamb, beef, roasted fowl, a tart and cheese with fruit. My house was clean and neat and my room had a good fire in it. We played cards after dinner and then had supper together, with wine and cold meat. My guests left at about 10 o'clock at night – both them and myself highly pleased with our day. I went to bed very tired.

14 January
Lay very long in bed, till with shame forced to rise.

Pepys' postcard to a pal

Imagine you are Samuel Pepys. Decorate the front of the postcard, adding the correct pictures. When you have completed the front, cut it out and write your message on the back. Use the sentences below to start.

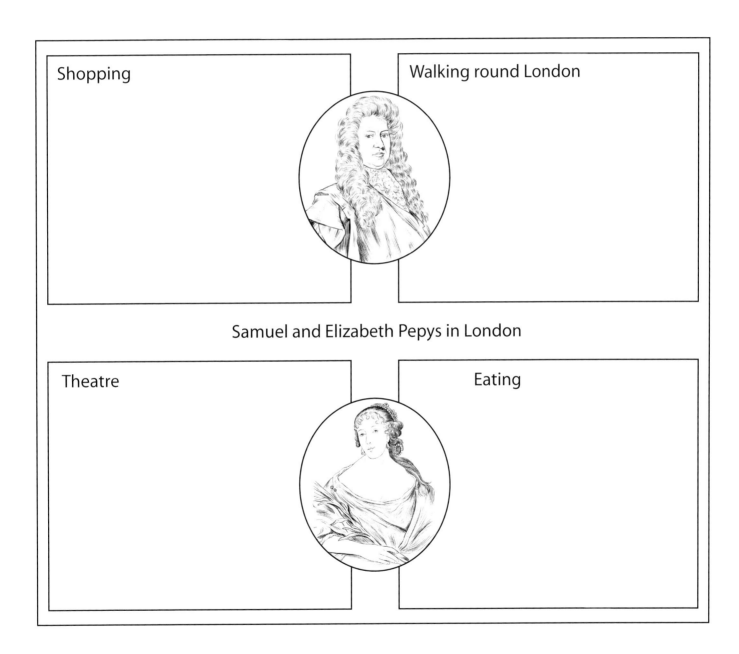

Shopping

Walking round London

Samuel and Elizabeth Pepys in London

Theatre

Eating

☞ Start your message like this:

Dear friend,

I am enjoying my time in London. There is plenty to do and to see...

History Changing Britain 1485–1750

Activity sheet – Mr and Mrs Pepys

Married life

Samuel Pepys' diary tells us a lot about his marriage. But what did his wife, Elizabeth, think? Read these extracts from Samuel's diary. Write **H** in the boxes where you think Samuel and Elizabeth were happy and **S** where you think they were sad.

13 October 1660

I went home, where I was angry with my wife because she leaves her things lying about. I kicked the little basket I bought her and broke it. ☐

10 October 1664

My wife and I have been married for nine years. Bless God for our long lives and loves and health together. I ask God from my heart for many more good years ahead. ☐

6 November 1660

I wanted to put the dog in the cellar because he keeps pooing in the house. My wife and I quarrelled about it. I will win this argument! ☐

19 December 1664

I was very angry with my wife for not looking after her servants properly. She gave me a cross answer and I hit her over her left eye, so hard that the poor wretch cried and was in pain. She tried to bite and scratch me. ☐

6 January 1663

I'm cross because my wife left her scarf, waistcoat and other things in the coach. (I admit that she did give them to me to look after, but it is still her fault that I forgot them.) ☐

4 March 1669

We went out for the first time in our coach and horses. We had a lovely afternoon. Tonight I am very pleased with my poor wife and look forward to the fun we will have in our coach this summer. ☐

History Changing Britain 1485–1750 © Folens (copiable page)

Elizabeth's letter

Now imagine you are Elizabeth. How did she feel about the events Samuel described?
Complete the letter from Elizabeth, showing her point of view.

Dear friend,

I am so fed up with Samuel! He is always in a bad mood. For example,_____
_____
_____

We quarrel about all sorts of things, like_____
_____
_____

Sometimes things get out of hand and Samuel is violent. For example_____
_____
_____

Luckily, we do have some good times together. One day we_____
_____
_____

Sometimes he even buys me lovely gifts_____
_____
_____

Your loving friend, Elizabeth

Teacher's notes

Disaster! Plague and fire

Objectives

- Consider the impact of major disasters on a 17th-century city
- Understand that people in the past responded to disasters with prejudice and limited understanding
- Demonstrate knowledge and understanding independently
- Collaborate and review learning

Prior knowledge

Students will have studied these disasters in primary school. They may also be aware of the dreadful plagues of the Middle Ages.

NC links

History skills 2a, 2b and 2e

Scottish attainment targets

Environmental Studies – Society – People in the past
Strand – People, events and societies of significance in the past
Level E
Strand – Change and continuity, cause and effect
Level E

Background

The Plague and the Great Fire are two of the most dramatic events in the history of 17th-century London. The Plague killed over 100 000 people in London and more in the countryside. Fleas carried by black rats spread it. The Plague raged throughout the summer and only declined as winter started.

London had always had lots of fires and at first witnesses were not impressed with the fire that broke out in September 1666 – for example, the Lord Mayor claimed, 'A woman could piss it out'.

Starter activities

Plague: To set the context for the lesson, ask students to write down <u>what</u> they know about the causes of disease and then ask them to write down <u>how</u> they know. This may help students to acknowledge that people in the past had different ideas, not because they were stupid, but because the technology for understanding how diseases spread was not available.

The Great Fire: Ask the students to imagine a fire destroying four-fifths of a nearby town. They could write down what they would expect to see, hear and smell as the fire burned. Encourage them also to write down what they would expect to happen once the fire had been put out.

Resource sheet and activity sheets

The tasks on the activity sheets 'Disaster! The Plague in London, 1665' and 'Trying to prevent or cure the Plague' are self-explanatory. Students will be able to see what Londoners thought caused the Plague, how Londoners tried to protect themselves from the disease and finally to distinguish between preventative actions and possible cures.

The resource sheet 'Disaster! The Great Fire of London, 1666' contains all the information the students need to complete the activity sheet, 'Disaster! The Great Fire quiz'. There are also some questions to promote thinking and discussion.

The activity sheet, 'Remember, remember!' provides students with an opportunity to demonstrate the knowledge they have gained during this programme of study. Emphasise the fact that they have had lots of opportunities to learn this material and that the questions are the same and appear in the same order as the ones they have been learning at home and in class. Successfully answering these questions is a significant achievement for lower-achieving students and will act as a morale and confidence booster.

Plenary

The assessment sheet can be used in a variety of ways to help students review their learning behaviour. Space has been left for you to target other behaviours for individuals or groups.

Disaster! The Plague in London, 1665

In 1665, an outbreak of the Plague in London killed approximately 100 000 people. This type of plague was caused by germs spread by the fleas that lived on black rats. The symptoms were horrible: large swellings developed in the armpits and groin or smaller spots arranged in a circle formed on the body. The Plague victim's temperature rose alarmingly. As many as 75% of everyone who got the Plague died within four days.

People in 1665 did not know about germs, so they did not understand what caused the Plague. People in the 17th century were not less intelligent than people in the 21st century. Why didn't they know about germs?

_____

_____

_____

To explain the Plague, they came up with some interesting ideas and some very odd ones. Some people believed their enemies (or the Jews or Catholics) had caused the Plague. Other causes are given in the table below.

☞ Can you think of reasons for these causes? Add them to the table.

People said the Plague was caused by:	Reason why they believed this:
Dry, warm weather	
Poisonous gases or bad smells	
Dogs	
Cats	
Comets	
The wrath of God	

☞ Imagine you are living in 1665. Make a poster warning people about the Plague.

● Tell people what you think causes the Plague.

● Tell them what the symptoms of the Plague are.

Activity sheet – Disaster! Plague and fire

Trying to prevent or cure the Plague

Write **P** in the prevention or cure column if you believe this describes a way of preventing the Plague.

Write **C** in the prevention or cure column if you believe this describes a way of curing the Plague.

Finally, decide if each method would actually work.

Method used in 1665	Prevention or cure? P or C	Would this work? Yes or No
Cover victims with mercury and put them in the oven		
Lock the Plague victims up in their houses for 40 days		
Carry flowers or use strong perfume		
Smoke or chew tobacco		
Sweat out the disease by drinking hot drinks		
Draw out the poison by putting a chicken's bottom against the victim's swellings		
Drink a potion made by a Plague doctor, like the 'Plague-water' Pepys was given		
Carry a lucky charm		
Kill the cats and dogs		
Use leeches to remove 'excess' blood		
Use laxatives to make the patient go to the toilet		
Keep away from people with the Plague by leaving town		

Disaster! The Great Fire of London, 1666

The causes of the Great Fire

The fire started in a baker's shop in Pudding Lane. Sparks set fire to the baker's wooden home. A servant tried to climb out of the building, but was too scared to jump from the roof. She was one of the few victims of the fire. Once it started, the fire spread quickly. Most of the buildings in London were made out of wood and the summer had been hot and dry. Strong winds blew the flames from one building to another. The fire was out of control.

The four days of Great Fire

People in London were used to fires and at first no one thought this fire was anything special. On the first night, Pepys took a look at the fire and went back to bed. However, this fire was different. The heat was so great that the lead roof on the old St Paul's Cathedral melted and flowed down the streets. People were shocked to see pigeons burning. Pepys was frightened that his house would burn, so he buried his important documents, his wine and a precious parmesan cheese in his garden. Lots of people left the city and watched the fire from safety.

Eventually the authorities decided to create 'fire breaks' by knocking down buildings in the path of the fire to prevent it spreading. This, together with a change in wind direction, meant that, after four days, the fire died out.

 What would you save if your house were threatened by a fire?

The results of the Great Fire

- About eight people died.
- Robert Hubert, a London watchmaker who was born in France, was blamed for the fire and executed in October 1666. (In fact, he wasn't even in London when the fire broke out.)
- The fire wiped out the Plague.
- In many places, the ground was too hot to walk on for several days afterwards.

- Traders and merchants lost their goods.
- No one had fire insurance, so many people were ruined and some moved away permanently.
- At least 65 000 people were made homeless by the fire. Rents soared in the unburnt area, but somehow accommodation was found for all who needed it.
- Five-sixths of the walled area of the city was destroyed. All the wooden buildings were reduced to ashes and only a few stone-built church towers remained.

 What do you think was the most important result of the fire?

History Changing Britain 1485–1750

Disaster! The Great Fire quiz

☞ Write your own quiz about the Great Fire.

Remember to include questions about the causes of the fire, what actually happened and the results of the fire.

Question	Answer
1.	
2.	
3.	
4.	
5.	
6.	
7.	
8.	
9.	
10.	

Test one of your friends and then test your teacher!

My friend got

_____

marks out of 10

My teacher got

_____

marks out of 10

History Changing Britain 1485–1750

Activity sheet – Disaster! Plague and fire

Remember, remember!

See how much you can remember about the 16th and 17th centuries. Write your answers on a separate piece of paper.

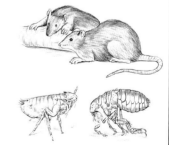

1. When did Henry VII become King?

2. When did Henry VIII become King?

3. Name two things Henry VIII was famous for.

4. What were Henry VIII's three children called (in age order)?

5. What happened to Henry VIII's six wives?

6. What religion was Edward VI?

7. Name two things Queen Mary was famous for.

8. Name two things Elizabeth I was famous for.

9. Why was Mary, Queen of Scots, executed?

10. What religion was Elizabeth I?

11. Who became King in 1603?

12. What was the 'Gunpowder Plot'?

13. What happened to the captured plotters?

14. What does the 'Divine Right of Kings' mean?

15. When did Charles I become King?

16. Why did Charles hate Parliament?

17. What is a civil war?

18. Why did Parliament win the Civil War?

19. When and why was Charles executed?

20. Who ruled England after Charles?

21. What happened when Cromwell died in 1658?

22. What happened in 1665?

23. What happened in London in 1666?

 How well did you do? I got ⬜ out of 23.

History Changing Britain 1485–1750

Assessment sheet

Are you always in the right place, at the right time? Do you have the right equipment and the right attitude?

I had a pen	I had a pencil	I listened to others	I worked well with a partner	I worked well in a group
I listened to my teachers	I spoke clearly, giving a full answer	I answered a question	I didn't call out	I asked for help
I thought before I spoke	I did not interrupt	I didn't disturb others	I stayed in my seat	I used the correct language
I asked a question	I understood the learning objectives	I completed all the tasks		

Use this page to help you think about how you learn and to identify the things you need to work on to do even better. Circle those statements you have achieved.

History Changing Britain 1485–1750